Captain Blackboot's Island

A play for children

Patricia Wood

Samuel French Ltd - London
New York-Toronto-Hollywood

ISBN 978-0-573-15208-5

www.samuelfrench-london.co.uk

www.samuelfrench.com

FOR AMATEUR PRODUCTION ENQUIRIES

UNITED KINGDOM AND WORLD EXCLUDING NORTH AMERICA

plays@SamuelFrench-London.co.uk
020 7255 4302/01

Each title is subject to availability from Samuel French, depending upon country of performance.

CHARACTERS

The Story-Teller
Captain Blackboot, an ex-pirate
The Mate
The Bosun
Oliver, an octopus
James } treasure-seekers
Sally }
Victoria, a sand-castle builder
Mrs Captain Blackboot
The Cook
Montague
Clara
Gregory
Liza
Samuel } Mrs Blackboot's children
Pansy
Percival
Egbert
Jemima
Captain Bloodshot, a Wicked Pirate
Mr Crossbones, his Mate
Wicked Pirates
People from the Friendly Island

The action takes place on a Deserted Island in a Sunny Southern Sea

NOTES ON THE PLAY

The play is very simple to stage. Any open space is satisfactory. It is also effective if the audience can be on three sides of the action.

Settings are minimal: a few rocks, one or two palm trees, although these are not necessary, and some "Treasure Trail" notices set up on sticks.

If a pianist is available, the excitement is increased by a few chords at the entrance of the Wicked Pirates, and during the fight. Simple tunes may be invented for the Ballad of the Wicked Pirates, the Children's Poem, and the two chants. These, however are not necessary, and they come over very well if spoken.

The groups of characters, the Pirates and the Blackboot children can be expanded or contracted according to the number of actors available.

If the play is to be cast with young children it is important that the Story-Teller be an adult, or an experienced older child.

CAPTAIN BLACKBOOT'S ISLAND

Scene 1

A Deserted Island in a Sunny Southern Sea

One or two palm trees and bushes dotted about give the place a homely air

The Story-Teller comes on to the Island and addresses the audience

Story-Teller Good afternoon. This is a deserted island in a sunny southern sea. You may have noticed these various signs which are dotted about on the island. These are sign-posts to a Treasure Trail. This Treasure Trail is the work of Captain Blackboot, an ex-pirate, and his mate and his bo'sun who have been living on this deserted island for some months. Captain Blackboot dreams of the day when his island will be famous, and so he has worked out this clever and complicated Treasure Trail, with the help of Oliver, his octopus friend. He has drawn three beautiful treasure maps, and these have been placed in empty ginger-beer bottles and thrown into the sea. Now, Captain Blackboot paces the sandy shore of his island waiting for Treasure-Seekers to arrive in their shiploads. Within hailing distance of Captain Blackboot's island, is another island on which live the Friendly People. Now, we don't happen to have enough actors to play the Friendly People, and we wondered whether you would be kind enough to do it for us? . . . You would? . . . Well, that's splendid. And now I'd better teach you the Friendly People's chant before we begin. It goes something like this.

The Story-Teller teaches the audience the Friendly People's chant

"Bacon and bananas in a coconut stew,
Make a super supper dish—for *you*!"

Well, you've learned that really splendidly. And I want you to remember that whenever the bo'sun calls out to the Friendly People, *you* must answer him with your Friendly People's chant. Shall we have a little rehearsal with the bo'sun? (*Calling*) Mr Bosun, would you mind coming here for a moment?

The Bosun enters, complete with telescope

Now then, Mr Bosun, these kind members of the audience have agreed to play the parts of the Friendly People, and we'd like to have a little rehearsal with you.

Bosun Delighted to oblige, I'm sure!

Story-Teller Good! Now, if you'd give your usual call to the Friendly People, Mr Bosun, we can reply with our little chant.

Bosun Rightyho! (*He climbs on to a rock, puts his telescope to his eye, and calls in a powerful voice*) Ahoy there! Friendly People!!

Story-Teller (*to the audience*) Now it's us!
"Bacon and bananas in a coconut stew,
Make a tasty supper dish—for *you*!!"
That was really *very* good indeed. Thank you, Mr Bosun and now the play can begin.

The Bosun stands on his rock looking out to sea through his telescope

The Mate enters and sits on the sand, holding a large Union Jack and an empty bottle, and Captain Blackboot comes on and begins striding about the island

Captain Blackboot (*striding about like anything*) Any sign of a ship, Mr Bosun?

Bosun No, sir, there ain't no sign, sir.

Captain Blackboot Shiver me timbers! I can't understand it! When did we throw them bottles into the sea, Mr Mate?

Mate Yesterday morning, Cap'n.

Captain Blackboot God bless me boots and buttons! Twenty-four hours and nobody's found them bottles with the treasure maps in!

Bosun That's right, sir, nobody ain't found 'em.

Captain Blackboot Three clean ginger-beer bottles, Mr Mate. Well corked down! *Was* they well corked down, Mr Mate?

Mate They was, Cap'n.

Captain Blackboot They ought to float!

Mate So they ought, sir.

Captain Blackboot Mizzle me main mast! They jolly well ought to float to the North Pole!

Bosun (*changing his telescope to the other eye*) Ay, ay, sir.
Mate Are there any people at the North Pole, Cap'n?
Captain Blackboot There's people everywhere, Mr Mate, if you looks for 'em. Take that island out there for instance. What's on it, Mr Mate?
Mate Why, there's Friendly People on that island, Cap'n.
Captain Blackboot That's right, Mr Mate. Just the same as you and me. Give 'em a friendly shout, Mr Bosun.
Bosun (*calling*) Ahoy there! Friendly People!
Friendly People (*chanting*) "Bacon and bananas in a coconut stew,
Make a tasty supper dish—for *you*!"
Captain Blackboot Friendly as anything, they are.
Mate I thought as 'ow we 'ad come to this 'ere island to get away from people, Cap'n.
Captain Blackboot To get away from *one* person Mr Mate. To get away from Mrs Lavinia Blackboot, my lady wife, and all 'er nine children.
Bosun She were a right one for talking, Cap'n.
Mate *And* for ordering folks about!
Captain Blackboot Ah, there comes a time when a man wants to be master in his own place. When a man wants a bit o' peace and quiet.
Bosun That's right, Cap'n.
Mate If it's peace and quiet we wants—why are we sending out maps inviting people to come to this island to search for treasure?
Captain Blackboot Dash me dusters, Mr Mate! What we wants is to be famous! Think of it—shiploads of treasure-seekers coming to Blackboot Island! We shall go down in history, Mr Mate.
Mate Ah, but what shall we give 'em to eat? There's only four kippers today. That's one each. What happens if a load of these treasure-seekers make fast on the beach?
Captain Blackboot Hammer down me hatches, Mr Mate! They'll bring their own sandwiches—treasure-seekers always do! And once they reads that treasure map, they'll be here in their thousands.
Mate That's what I'm afraid of
Captain Blackboot Cheer up, Mr Mate! It's the price of fame! See how the Bosun is looking forward to it. Ain't you, Mr Bosun? (*He claps the Bosun hard the on back*)

Bosun (*choking slightly*) Ay, ay, sir.

Captain Blackboot (*taking out a large watch and consulting it*) Lower me lanyard! It's six bells! Time for the ceremony of the flag! Mr Bosun!

Bosun Sir?

Captain Blackboot Whistle up the crew.

Bosun Ay, ay, sir. (*He blows his whistle*)

An Octopus comes out from behind a clump of bushes. He carries two feather dusters

Captain Blackboot Ah, there you are, Oliver. Time for the ceremony of the flag.

Oliver Very good, Cap'n. I'll do me dusting afterwards.

The Mate carefully places the bottles upright in the sand, and stands the Union Jack in it. Then the Three ex-Pirates and Oliver stand to attention beside the flag

Captain Blackboot Are you all ready?

Bosun
Mate } Ay, ay, sir. (*Speaking together*)
Oliver

Captain Blackboot Then, together with the departed spirits of our old shipmates, we'll sing the dear old song.

Story-Teller Just a moment, Cap'n Blackboot. I'm sorry to interrupt, but I'm afraid we shall need a bit of help from the audience with this song. (*To the audience*) We shall want you to sing for the departed spirits of their old shipmates. Do you know "Rule, Britannia"? Oh, well, perhaps we'd just better rehearse it a couple of times.

They do so

That's all right then, Cap'n Blackboot. Can we have your line again?

Captain Blackboot Right you are. Now then—together with the departed spirits of our old shipmates, we'll sing the dear old song. Ready? One, two, three, go . . .!

All (*waving Union Jacks if they have got them, and singing*)
"Rule, Britannia,
Britannia rule the waves,
Britons never, never, never, shall be slaves!"

Captain Blackboot Strike your colours, Mr Mate.

The Mate takes the flag out of the bottle

Back on watch, Mr Bosun.

The Bosun goes back to his rock

Suffering sharks, Oliver! You were a bit flat this morning!

Oliver Sorry, Cap'n. I've got a bit of a cold. Any sign of treasure-seekers, Cap'n?

Captain Blackboot Not a sausage, Oliver. Not a sausage.

Oliver Waste of time, all that treasure-trail and map making. I said so all along and I'll say so again. We should be getting on with building a hut, that's what we should be doing. It was cold last night on the beach, and I don't feel none too good this morning. Atishoo!

Captain Blackboot You want to look after that cold, Oliver. You watch it or your ink will go pale! We shall need plenty of it soon, to make more maps.

Oliver (*disgustedly*) Maps! Lot of nonsense, that's what it is.

Captain Blackboot That reminds me, Oliver. I suppose your ink *is* waterproof? I mean, it wouldn't wash off or anything?

Oliver (*indignantly*) Well, I like that! My special octopus ink what takes me months to manufacture, and you ask if it's waterproof?

Captain Blackboot Well, *is* it?

Oliver (*very dignified*) If the Emperor of China was to write his name in the sea with my ink, it would stay there as clear as clear until the next tide!

Captain Blackboot (*clapping Oliver on the shoulder*) That's good enough for me, Oliver!

Bosun (*waving his telescope about wildly*) Cap'n, Cap'n! A sail! A sail!

Captain Blackboot (*joining the Bosun on the rock and snatching the telescope from him*) Where, Mr Bosun? Where?

Bosun On the starboard bow, Cap'n! They're making for Skelington Bay!

Captain Blackboot So they are, Mr Bosun! Polish me plimsolls! You and the mate go across and meet them. I'll brush me hair! And pipe 'em aboard, Mr Bosun. Pipe 'em aboard!

Bosun Ay, ay, sir!

The Mate and the Bosun hurry off to meet the visitors

Captain Blackboot Look sharp, Oliver, and dust things up a bit. We've got visitors! Make everything look ship shape!
Oliver (*gloomily*) That's all very well, Cap'n, but I've only four pairs of arms!

Oliver goes about dusting the various signs and rocks

Captain Blackboot (*combing his hair*) Now then, Oliver, shall I sit or stand?
Oliver I beg your pardon sir?
Captain Blackboot Will it look better if I'm sitting down when they come in, or standing up?
Oliver I should behave natural if I was you, Cap'n. It's all a lot of nonsense, that's what it is.

The Mate and the Bosun appear, escorting three treasure-seekers. These are James, a boy of nine, Sally who is eight, and their younger sister Victoria who is six. James carries a treasure map, Sally an empty ginger-beer bottle, and Victoria a bucket and spade

Mate Cap'n Blackboot, sir! The Treasure-Seekers! Their names is as follows. James, Sally, and er- er . . .
Victoria My name is Victoria. Is this *your* island?
Captain Blackboot It is.
Victoria It's not very big, is it?
Sally Don't be rude, Victoria! (*To Captain Blackboot*) It's a very *nice* island!
Captain Blackboot Thank you, miss.
Sally Are you the only people here?
Captain Blackboot Except for the Friendly People on that island over there (*He indicates the audience*)
Children Friendly People?
Captain Blackboot That's right!—Give 'em a shout, Mr Bosun.
Bosun (*calling*) Ahoy there! Friendly People!
Friendly People "Bacon and bananas in a coconut stew,
Make a super supper dish—for *you*!"
James They sound friendly enough.
Victoria Your island has got quite a lot of sand, can I make sandcastles?
Sally (*correcting her*) "*May* I make sandcastles."
Victoria (*repeating obediently*) *May* I make sandcastles?
James No you may *not*! You promised you'd be quiet if we

brought you with us—so *be* quiet! We have things to discuss with the Captain.

Captain Blackboot If the young lady wishes to make sandcastles, we don't object. (*Calling*) Oliver!

Oliver (*coming over*) Yes, sir?

Captain Blackboot Take the young lady over there—(*he points to some rocks*)—and help her to make sandcastles.

Oliver Excuse me, Cap'n, I don't know how to make sand-castles.

Victoria (*grabbing one of his eight arms*) I'll show you—come on!

Victoria and Oliver exit

James Good, that's got rid of her. Now then, Captain—about this treasure.

Captain Blackboot Ah, you've come to dig for the treasure, 'ave you?

James That's right.

Sally We found this ginger-beer bottle with your treasure map in it.

Captain Blackboot It didn't get wet, I hope?

James Dry as a bone.

Sally It took us simply ages to get the cork out.

Mate Well, we bashed it in with a rock, you see miss.

James So here we are, and we want to search for the treasure.

Captain Blackboot Skuttle me skuppers! You're as welcome as the flowers in May. Ain't they, Mr Bosun?

Bosun Ay, ay, sir.

Captain Blackboot It's all laid out for you as neat as ninepence. All you have to do is read the map, and then follow the little signs. Ain't that right, Mr Mate?

Mate Ay, sir, that's right.

Captain Blackboot So me and my crew, we'll lay off-shore and have a pipe o' baccy. You just take your time and enjoy yourselves.

Sally Thank you very much.

Captain Blackboot, the Mate and Bosun exit. James spreads the map out on a rock

I wonder what the treasure will be? Do you think lots of jewels like emeralds and rubies and things? Or will it be a chest filled with gold coins?

James We'll never know if you don't stop chattering.
Sally Well, whatever the treasure is, I think we should give some of it to that nice Captain Blackboot.
James Let's concentrate on the map. I'll read out the first clue. (*He reads*)
"You starts with the rock which is marked with a 'D',
Then you takes three paces towards the sea."
Sally Oh, it's in poetry—how lovely! Look James, here's a rock with the letter "D" painted on it!
James So there is. Now then, three paces. Ready? One, two, three!
Sally What next?
James (*reading*)
"Seventy little oyster shells laid in a row,
Points to the way you wants to go!"
Sally (*excitedly*) Here they are! Going off in that direction!

The Mate enters carrying two spades

Mate Cap'n Blackboot's compliments, and you'll need these presently for the digging.
Sally Thank you very much. Isn't it exciting?
James It will be when we find the treasure. Come on!

The Mate exits, and Sally and James march off L, counting oyster shells as they go

Children One, two, three, four . . .

For a moment the island is quiet and the beach deserted

Then with evil cries and ugly cutlasses, the Wicked Pirates make their way on to the beach.

Wicked Pirates Arggggh! Urgggggh! Dang me! etc.

The Story-Teller comes forward

Story-Teller (*stopping the Wicked Pirates*) Just a moment, please. Do you mind?

The Wicked Pirates stop saying "Argggh" and "Urgggh", and listen quietly

(*To the audience*) Now, you must have noticed that these are

Wicked Pirates. You did notice it, didn't you? . . . Good. Well, as they are such *very* Wicked Pirates, I should like you to hiss and boo them when they come on. Will you do that? . . . Splendid! (*To the Wicked Pirates*) I'm awfully sorry, but would you mind very much coming on again? Thank you.

The Wicked Pirates go off

Now, as soon as they come on, start hissing. (*Calling out to the Wicked Pirates*) We're ready when you are!

The Wicked Pirates come on again

When the hissing and booing has died down a bit, the Wicked Pirates wave their ugly cutlasses at the audience and say their beastly ballad

THE BEASTLY BALLAD OF THE WICKED PIRATES

Wicked Pirates Oh, we're not very nice,
Not nice at all,
We're nastier than you think!
We'll cut your throat for tuppence,
And leave your ship to sink!
Oh, we'll 'ave your guts for garters,
So just mind what you do!
With a rum tum tiddle iddle oh, ho, ho,
We're Captain Bloodshot's crew!

Oh, we're not very bright,
Not bright at all,
We're stupider than we look!
We've never wrote a letter,
Nor read a blooming book!
But we'll hang you from the yard-arm,
So just mind what you do!
With a rum tum tiddle iddle oh, ho, ho,
We're Captain Bloodshot's crew!

Captain Bloodshot Simmer down, me 'earties! Mr Crossbones, is this the place?

Mr Crossbones The very same, Cap'n.

Captain Bloodshot Then we'll melt into the background until night do come. Roll up the Treasure Map and hide the ginger-beer bottle, Mr Crossbones. I don't wish to fall foul o' Cap'n Blackboot—but I'll 'ave 'is treasure if it's the last thing I do!

Laughing evilly, the Wicked Pirates melt away and hide. Oliver comes out from behind a rock and settles down for a little snooze. Victoria comes looking for him

Victoria Come *on*, Oliver—you're not digging. How do you think we'll get down to Australia if you don't help me dig?
Oliver I thought you was doing very nicely by yourself, miss.
Victoria But I *want* you to help me! First I want you to find a nice big flag to put on my sandcastle.
Oliver A flag, miss?
Victoria Yes, a big one. That one over there will do. (*She points to the Union Jack which is lying in the sand*)
Oliver Oh, you can't have that one miss. That's a very special flag, that is.
Victoria (*stamping her foot*) But I *want* it!
Oliver I'm sorry miss, but you can't have it. The Mate wouldn't like it. Nor would the Bosun. And as for Cap'n Blackboot, he'd chop you up into little bits if you so much as laid a finger on that flag.

Victoria bursts into loud and noisy tears

The Captain, Mate and Bosun come hurrying in

Captain Blackboot Now then, Oliver. What's all this?
Oliver The little girl wants the flag, sir. To put on her sandcastle.
Captain Blackboot The *flag*?
Victoria (*pointing*) Yes. That flag over there.
Mate But that's a very special kind of flag, miss. We only sets that flag up when we're going to sing.
Victoria Well, sing now—I want to hear you.

The Captain sighs and raises his eyes to heaven

Captain Blackboot Mr Bosun, is it eight bells?

The Bosun licks his finger and holds it up into the wind

Bosun As near as maybe, Cap'n.
Captain Blackboot Then run up the flag, Mr Mate.

The Mate sets up the flag and they stand to attention beside it. Victoria sits on the sand watching with great interest

Together with the departed spirits of our shipmates, we will sing the dear old song. Ready?

Crew Ay, ay, sir.
Captain Blackboot Then one, two, three, go!

The Crew and the Audience sing a chorus of "Rule Britannia"

Victoria Sing it again!
Captain Blackboot We *never* sing it more than once at a time.
Victoria (*stamping her foot*) Sing it again—I *like* it!
Mate We can't do that, miss.
Victoria Sing it again, or I shall *cry*!

Very hastily they start singing again

As they reach the second line James and Sally run on. They are hot, dusty and very, very cross

James Here they are! (*He throws the map down at the Captain's feet and folds his arms.*) Well, *that* was a fraud, if you like! "Dig at the spot marked X and you'll find the treasure!"
Sally And we *did* dig at the spot marked X, and all we found was an empty chest!
James Nothing in it at all!
Sally Not even a single ruby!
James So what have you got to say about *that*?

Victoria goes quietly back to her digging

Captain Blackboot (*very pleased*) You found the chest, did you?
James Oh yes. We found the chest.
Captain Blackboot I told you it was a good map. Didn't I say so Oliver? I said it was a good map.
Oliver Yes, Cap'n, so you did.
Captain Blackboot (*pacing up and down and very pleased with himself*) I knew I could make a good treasure map if I tried. I knew it! What did you think of the poetry bits? They were good, weren't they?
James Never mind the poetry, what about the treasure?
Captain Blackboot (*not listening to him*) And the dear old chest was still there, was it? It hadn't rotted away, or got damp or anything?
Sally Never mind about the chest—what about the treasure?
Captain Blackboot There ain't no treasure, matey. Ain't none now nor never was. Is that so, Mr Bosun?

Bosun Ay, ay, Cap'n. That's so all right.
Mate Don't tell us you was expecting to find *real* treasure?
James (*indignantly*) Of course we were!
Mate Well, fancy that now!
Sally You made a treasure map—what's a treasure map for if it doesn't lead you to some treasure?
Bosun Well, it's like this, you see, miss. We ain't got no treasure.
Captain Blackboot You're not *really* cross, are you?
James Of course we are! Why do you think we came all this way if it wasn't to find some treasure?

Captain Blackboot sits sadly on a rock and puts his head in his hands

Captain Blackboot Oh dear, oh dear, oh dear, oh dear.
Oliver You've upset the Cap'n now.
Captain Blackboot Oh dear, oh dear, oh dearie, dearie, dearie, dear!
Bosun He's upset all right.
Captain Blackboot Oh dearie dear, oh dearie, dearie, dearie dear!
Mate There's no mistake about it, he's upset! Poor soul, 'twill take him a long time to get over this.
Bosun He'll be a changed man, he will. A changed man.
Oliver It was the Cap'n's dream to make this island as famous as the Treasure Island what's wrote about in books.
Bosun Months and months it took us to make that treasure trail.
Mate Months and months of hard labour.
Oliver And what about all the ink I provided for the maps and notices?
Bosun Quite pale, Oliver was, after giving all that ink. It was pitiful to see him.

The Captain sighs again. James and Sally begin to feel sorry for him

Mate He's had a 'ard life.
Oliver *She* drove 'im to it, you know.
Sally Who drove him to it?
Mate Mrs Captain Blackboot, his lady wife.
Bosun *And* her nine children.
Mate That there woman would drive a man to drink.

Bosun But the Cap'n, 'e ain't a drinking man, so 'e ran away instead. And being 'is shipmates, you see—we come with 'im.
Mate Peaceful it's been, living 'ere. Like 'eaven. And the Captain, 'e blossomed like a rose.

The Captain sobs loudly

Oliver He's a broken man now. It's all over.
Victoria (*calling*) Oliver, come here and help me with this digging.
Sally Don't be tiresome, Victoria.
Victoria (*hurrying over*) But he *must* come! I've dug down to a bit of Australia, and it's all hard and knobbly, and I can't get it up by myself!
James Don't be so silly, Victoria. You couldn't possibly have dug down to Australia.
Victoria Well, I *have*. And everything's made of gold. And there's necklaces and sparkly things in Australia. But my arms won't reach down to pull them up.
Oliver Necklaces?
Bosun Gold?
Mate Come on, me hearties, she's found some treasure!

They all rush to the place where Victoria was digging. Only Captain Blackboot remains where he was. He has not even opened his eyes

All (*excitedly calling out instructions to one another*) Here, see if you can reach—I've got hold of something—steady on, it might break—wait a minute—hand them up, can't you?—I say, look at this—let's show the Captain!

They hurry from behind the rock, their arms filled with treasure, and pour it into a heap in front of the Captain

Captain, look what we've found—*real* treasure!

The Captain opens his eyes and stares at the heap of treasure. He runs his hands through some of the jewels, then, slowly he stands up

Captain Blackboot Batten down me hatches! We'll be a proper Treasure Island! I'll be as famous as Long John Silver! To work, everyone, we must make more maps! Oliver, can you rustle up some more ink?

Oliver And proud to do it, Cap'n. Though I don't say as 'ow it will be easy—not so soon after the last lot.
Sally May we stay and help you make more maps? We'd like to. We don't need to go back to school until next week.
Captain Blackboot Glad to have you aboard, maties! But, rattle me rowing boats, it's almost nine bells. Mr Mate, the flag!

The flag is set up. All stand to attention

Shipmates all, we sing the song tonight in a spirit of thanksgiving for our good fortune. One, two, three . . .
All (*singing*) "Rule, Britannia . . ."
Victoria (*interrupting the singing*) There's a ship coming into the bay!
Sally Hush, Victoria.
Victoria But there *is* a ship—with lots of people in it!

The singing stops and everyone shades their eyes with their hands in order to peer out to sea

Bosun She's right, Cap'n There's a vessel on the starboard bow.
Mate Making for Skelington Bay, Cap'n.
Captain Blackboot Splice me spinaker, it's the second ginger-beer bottle! Someone's gone and picked it up and read the map. Hide this! (*He points to the treasure*) We'll put it in the chest later on. Stand to attention, shipmates, and welcome our visitors. Fame at last!

Oliver, Victoria, Sally and James hide the treasure behind the rocks then they stand to attention with the others

A thin, untidy-looking woman, wrapped in shawls and decorated with hair curlers comes on from the direction of skeleton bay. She is accompanied by the Cook, who carries a rolling pin, and nine scowling Children

The Woman (*in a shrill voice*) Is that you, Ebenezer Blackboot? Ha, I thought so! Caught you at last, have we?

There is a moment's horrified silence

Mate (*trembling*) God bless my soul—it's Mrs Cap'n Blackboot.
Captain Blackboot (*in a small, terrified voice*) Is that you, Lavinia my dear?

Mrs Blackboot (*advancing and waving her umbrella*) Don't you "my dear" me, Ebenezer Blackboot! Ran off, did you? Thought you'd got away from me, did you? Well, I've found you at last, and you won't get so far next time! Children, say "hello" to your Pa!

The Children advance towards Captain Blackboot in a line and repeat their little poem

CHILDREN'S POEM

Mrs Blackboot's Children Hello Pa,
Here we are,
We've come a long way to find you!
When you sailed for a foreign shore,
You went and left us behind you!

Hello Dad,
Ain't you glad
We followed through storm and
through rain?
We know we've been missed,
So we'd like to be kissed!
Oh, say you won't leave us again!

Mrs Blackboot Ain't you going to kiss 'em, Ebenezer?
Captain Blackboot Not just at the moment, my dear. I've—I've got a bit of a cold.

Oliver sneezes loudly

Mrs Blackboot Colds eh? You don't look healthy, any of you. I'll rub all your chests with camphorated oil tonight! Meanwhile, we'll have this place tidied up.
Cook Ain't fit to be seen, it ain't.
Mrs Blackboot And what's this nasty slimy octopus doing here? Cook! Get rid of it!
Cook Yes, mum. Go on, off with you! Shoo! (*She attacks Oliver with her rolling pin*) Back to the jungle where you belong!
Mate (*stepping forward*) Now listen to me, my good woman!
Cook Don't you "good woman" me! Get all this sea-weed picked up and throw it back in the sea! How anyone can live in such a pig-sty I'm sure I don't know! I dreads to think, mum, what a state their cooking-stove will be in!

Montague (*whining*) Ma, I'm 'ungry!
Clara Ain't we going to 'ave supper, Ma?
Gregory I don't like it 'ere, Ma.
Liza Where we going to sleep, Ma?
Samuel Ma, I'm cold.
Pansy It's getting dark, Ma, and I'm frightened.
Percival I wish we was back at 'ome, Ma.
Egbert There's a nasty noise out there, Ma.
Jemima A thumping and bumping noise, Ma.
Children You listen, Ma.

Everyone listens. The jolly sound of music can be heard coming faintly across the water

Mrs Blackboot Ebenezer Blackboot, what's that nasty thumping and bumping what's a-frightening of the children?
Captain Blackboot Why my dear, that's only the Friendly People on the next island having a bit of a party. Give 'em a shout, Mr Bosun.
Bosun Ay, ay, sir. Ahoy there! Friendly People!
Friendly People "Bacon and bananas in a coconut stew,
Make a tasty supper dish, for *you*!"

All the Children burst into tears

Mrs Blackboot There, there, my preciousnesses. Did their wicked father make them live on a desert island, then? Never mind! (*To Captain Blackboot*) Now then, where's the hut?
Captain Blackboot The what?
Mrs Blackboot The hut, Ebenezer. The place where we sleep! Cook and me is going to take these dear children and put them all to bed. They're wore out after a day at sea—ain't you my lambs?

The Children sob noisily

Be quiet, the lot of you! Now then, where's the hut?
Captain Blackboot (*clearing his throat*) I'm afraid, my love, that there . . .

The Mate quickly moves in between Mrs Blackboot and the Captain. He nudges Captain Blackboot very *sharply with his elbow, clears his throat, and smiles upon Mrs Blackboot*

Mate (*very loudly*) What the Captain is trying to say, ma'am, is—

the hut's round the other side of the island. You and the children, bless their innocent 'earts, will be safe and cosy round there! It's just at the end of that path there. (*He points off* R) You can't miss it, ma'am. And the rest of us will stay 'ere and clear up the beach so as it's all ship-shape for you in the morning.

Cook (*waving her rolling pin at him*) Well, see that it is!

Mrs Blackboot Montague, Clara, Gregory, Liza, Samuel, Pansy, Percival, Egbert, Jemima! Follow me!

Children Yes, Ma.

Mate Off to the right, ma'am—that's the way!

Mrs Blackboot, the Cook and the Children march off

Captain Blackboot But, Mr Mate—there ain't no hut on this Island!

Mate *You* know that, sir. And *I* know that! But Mrs Cap'n Blackboot, *she* don't know that. And while she's a-looking for what ain't there, I suggests, Cap'n, that we scarper!

Oliver He's right Cap'n. We can spend the night on the Friendly People's Island. After all, when Mrs Cap'n Blackboot finds there ain't no hut, she'll be off in her boat at first light, taking the children with her. *Then* we shall 'ave the island to ourselves again.

James It's a splendid idea, Captain. We can go in *our* boat.

Oliver What do you say, Cap'n?

Captain Blackboot We'll do it! All hands to the pump and lower the sheets! We're off to the Friendly People's Island!

Bosun Cap'n Blackboot, sir!

Captain Blackboot What is it, Mr Bosun?

Bosun It's nearly ten bells, sir.

Captain Blackboot So it is, Mr Bosun! Mr Mate, hold the Flag aloft, and we'll sing as we go!

The procession winds out of sight to the Friendly People's Island singing "Rule, Britannia" as they go. After a moment, Captain Bloodshot, Mr Crossbones and the wicked pirates creep on to the beach

Captain Bloodshot That's got rid of old Blackboot and his crew. Are they out of sight, Mr Crossbones?

Mr Crossbones (*looking*) Out of sight, Cap'n Bloodshot.

Captain Bloodshot So, now for the treasure. Spread out and search every inch of the island.
Crew Ay, ay, sir!

The Wicked Pirates sneak off on their hunt for the treasure

Story-Teller I wonder if you noticed what I noticed? Cap'n Blackboot forgot to take the treasure with him, didn't he? I wonder what's going to happen about that? Anyway, while he's rowing to the Friendly People's Island, and Mrs Cap'n Blackboot and the children are looking for the hut that isn't there, we'll take a little break. Come back in about a quarter of an hour, and we'll see what happens next!

CURTAIN

SCENE 2

The same

The Story-Teller enters

Story-Teller Ah, you're all back I see. Well, while you were gone I did a bit of thinking. Now, do you remember that we left the Wicked Pirates looking for the treasure? You do? And it *is* Cap'n Blackboot's treasure, isn't it? Because it was found on his island, and we don't want the Wicked Pirates to get it, do we? No! So it seems to me that Cap'n Blackboot and his friends might need a bit of help later on, if it comes to a fight. And we'd like to help them, wouldn't we? Yes, of course we would. Now for most of the play you've all been acting as Friendly People, and *very* good you've been! But I happen to know that Captain Bloodshot and his crew are absolutely terrified of Nasty People! So I wondered if *you* would mind acting as Nasty People, in case we need to frighten the Wicked Pirates away. Would you mind doing that? You *wouldn't*? Oh, that's splendid. Then I think we'd better rehearse a Nasty Person's chant, so as to be ready for anything.

The Story-Teller and the audience practise a nasty person's chant

"Rattle snake and shark's teeth!
What a lot we've got!
Catch the Wicked Pirates
And drown the blooming lot!
Zing, zing, rattle, rattle, yah! yah!! YAH!!!!"

You really are awfully good. Now I think we're ready for anything. But, ssh! I think I hear someone coming.

Mrs Blackboot, the Cook and the Children walk wearily on

Cook It ain't no use, mum, I can't walk no farther. It's me bunions, mum. It's like as if they was on fire!

Mrs Blackboot Stop grumbling, Cook! We've got to go on until we find the hut. Look at these dear innocent children. *They're* not grumbling!

Children (*immediately starting to grumble furiously*) I'm tired, Ma—why don't we go home?—I want a jam sandwich, Ma—Ma, *can't* we go home? This sand is all scratchy on my feet, Ma—Ma, Percival pushed me!—I never pushed her, Ma! What's a bunion, Ma?—I'm ever so hungry, Ma!, etc.

Mrs Blackboot Be quiet, the lot of you, and let me think! Now then Cook, which way did we come?

Cook (*pointing off* R) That way, mum.

Mrs Blackboot (*pointing off* L) Then *that's* the way we must go.

Montague Mum, we've been round here before.

Mrs Blackboot Don't be silly, Montague.

Montague Yes we have, mum. That's my lollipop what I dropped.

Mrs Blackboot Don't talk nonsense, Montague. Now, we must go on until we find this hut. Cook, can't you get them singing something?

Cook I don't know as 'ow I *can* sing with me bunions on fire, but I'll 'ave a go.

Cook starts them singing "The Grand Old Duke of York" as they wearily march off L

Montague (*as they go*) That *is* my lollipop, Ma! Ma, that *is* my lollipop!

The Children's voices fade into the distance and on come Bloodshot and his crew

Mr Crossbones No sign o' the treasure, Cap'n.

The Wicked Pirates sink down on to the sand in a state of sadness and despair

Captain Bloodshot Blast me bilges! What a cross-eyed, bandy-legged, thick 'eaded crew you are! I brings you to an island where there's treasure—I asts you to find it and all you can say is "There ain't no sign of it, cap'n!" (*He draws his cutlass and strides about among them*) Butter me battenburg, I'll cut off your eyebrows—I'll pulverise your periwigs—I'll—I'll—I'll . . .

A Young Pirate comes out from behind a rock carrying a golden goblet

Young Pirate Excuse me, Cap'n Bloodshot, sir—is this treasure?

Captain Bloodshot (*snatching the goblet from him*) Is this treasure, he asts? I'll say it's treasure, you miserable little monster, you! Where did you find it, eh? Speak up!

Young Pirate Behind them rocks, Cap'n.

Captain Bloodshot Behind them rocks, 'e says. Behind them rocks! Come on, you lazy, lumbering, lunatics! Let's get it before Blackboot comes back!!

With yells of delight the Wicked Pirates disappear behind the far rocks. Silence

Captain Blackboot and his party enter quarrelling

Captain Blackboot Polish me pistols, I don't ask for much. Not much I don't ask for! Who was the thick-'eaded numbskull what forgot to bring the treasure?

Mate You never told us to bring it, Cap'n.

Captain Blackboot Course I never told you to bring it! Course I never! Your own common sense should 'ave told you! What was you thinking about, Oliver, to leave 'undreds of pounds worth of treasure lying about on the sand?

Oliver I'm sorry, Cap'n—it's my cold. It's made me thick-headed, like! (*He sneezes*)

Captain Blackboot Well, go and fetch it then! I can't spend all night rowing backwards and forwards to the Friendly People's Island. Go and fetch it before Mrs Lavinia Blackboot gets 'er 'ands on it!

The Mate and the Bosun are just starting towards the far rocks when out from behind them come Bloodshot, Crossbones and the Wicked Pirates. Their arms are filled with treasure. Each party of Pirates stands perfectly still for a moment, sizing up the other. Captain Blackboot is the first to recover

(*Drawing his cutlass*) Aha!

Captain Bloodshot (*drawing his cutlass*) Aha!
Captain Blackboot So it's you, Bloodshot!
Captain Bloodshot That's right, Blackboot!
Captain Blackboot Aha!
Captain Bloodshot Aha!
Captain Blackboot I'd be obliged, Bloodshot, if you'll tell your crew to 'and over my treasure!
Captain Bloodshot *Your* treasure, Blackboot?
Captain Blackboot *My* treasure, Bloodshot!

The two Captains cautiously circle around each other

Captain Bloodshot One step towards this booty, Blackboot, and you're a dead man!
Captain Blackboot We'll see about that, Bloodshot!—Mr Mate, Mr Bosun!

The Mate and the Bosun draw their cutlasses

Captain Bloodshot Mr Crossbones, tell the crew to draw!
Mr Crossbones Ay, ay, sir!

The Wicked Pirates drop the treasure they are holding and draw cutlasses. The Pirate Chiefs and their crews continue to circle cautiously around one another. In the distance can be heard the sound of "The Grand Old Duke of York"

Mrs Blackfoot, the Cook and the Children enter in a straggly line, still singing

Captain Bloodshot What's this, what's this? Women and children?
Captain Blackboot Watch your words, Bloodshot! That is Mrs Lavinia Blackboot, my lady wife, and all my nine off-spring!
Captain Bloodshot Mr Crossbones—take the women and children prisoners!
Mr Crossbones Ay, ay, sir!

Mr Crossbones and some of the Wicked Pirates grab Captain Blackboot's family. The Children scream, Mrs Blackboot hurls abuse at Mr Crossbones, and the Cook fights manfully with her rolling pin

Captain Blackboot (*seeing red*) I'll make spaghetti of the lot of you! Hands off my family!

Hand-to-hand fighting breaks out. Mrs Blackboot, the Cook and Children, guarded by a couple of Wicked Pirates huddle in one corner

James, Sally and Victoria enter and join in the fighting, but it is plain that Captain Blackboot and his crew are out-numbered

Oliver escapes from the fighting pirates and comes to the edge of the stage

Oliver It's time I got some help! Ahoy there, Friendly People! are you ready to be Nasty People and frighten the Wicked Pirates? You are? Good! Then let's start the Nasty Person's chant. A few of you had better come up here so that you're a bit closer!

The audience starts the Nasty Person's chant and Oliver fetches some of them up on to the stage and leads them among the Pirates

Oliver and the Audience
"Rattle snake and shark's teeth!
What a lot we've got!
Catch the Wicked Pirates,
And drown the blooming lot!
Zing, zing, rattle, rattle, yah! yah!! YAH!!!"

The chant gets louder and louder and nastier and nastier. Captain Bloodshot begins to tremble in his boots

Captain Bloodshot What's that I hear? Mr Crossbones, is it the chant of Nasty Persons?

Mr Crossbones (*also trembling in his boots*) I believe it is, Cap'n Bloodshot, sir!

Captain Bloodshot (*unable to stand any more*) Mr Crossbones, bring the crew and we'll scarper! If there's one thing I can't abide, it's Nasty People!

The Wicked Pirates take to their heels, and run, and everyone boos and hisses as they go

Captain Blackboot (*when all is quiet again*) Well, Oliver, my lad, that was a clever thing you did.

Oliver (*sneezing*) I'd have done more, Cap'n, if it weren't for my cold.

Mrs Blackboot (*coming forward*) I'll rub your chest with camphorated oil tonight, Oliver. I've quite taken to you. I'll rub everyone's chest with camphorated oil! What you want is a woman to look after you! Now then, Ebenezer Blackboot, tell me the truth. Is there a hut on this island, or ain't there?

Captain Blackboot Well, my dear, it's like this . . .

Mrs Blackboot I thought so. Well, you'd better get to work, all of you, and build one!

Captain Blackboot Well my dear, perhaps you're right. It does get a bit cold on the beach of a night time.

Mrs Blackboot (*severely*) Of course I'm right! We'll be comfortable and happy on this Island if it's the last thing we do!

Everybody cheers

Bosun (*licking his finger and holding it up*) Excuse me, Cap'n Blackboot, according to the direction of the wind, it must be eleven bells!

Captain Blackboot Eleven bells, eh? Then raise the flag, Mr Mate, and we will sing, together with the departed spirits of our old shipmates, the dear old song.

Crew Ay, ay, Cap'n.

The Mate sets the flag up in the bottle. The Crew, the Blackboot Family, James, Sally and Victoria, stand to attention and sing

"Rule, Britannia,
Britannia rule the waves!
Britons never, never, never, shall be slaves!!'

The Story-teller comes forward

Story-Teller So it looks as if it will work out all right. Mrs Lavinia Blackboot and the Cook will look after them, and cook their meals. The children will play in the sand, and Cap'n Blackboot and his crew can work away at making a new Treasure Trail. *This* time with *real* treasure at the end of it. I expect Sally, Victoria and James will visit the Island in the school holidays, and with any luck, Oliver won't get any more colds. Thank you very much for helping with our play! Good-bye!

CURTAIN

FURNITURE AND PROPERTY LIST

On stage: Rocks
Palm trees—optional
"Treasure-Trail" notices on sticks
Sand
Oyster shells
Hidden behind rocks or bushes: 2 feather dusters, jewels, goblets, plates, ornaments and other articles of "treasure"

Off stage: Telescope (**Bosun**)
Union Jack (**Mate**)
Empty bottle (**Mate**)
Treasure map (**James**)
Empty ginger-beer bottle (**Sally**)
Bucket, spade (**Victoria**)
2 spades (**Mate**)
Cutlasses (**Pirates, Mate, Bosun, Blackboot, Bloodshot**)
Rolling pin (**Cook**)
Umbrella (**Mrs Blackboot**)

Personal: **Captain Blackboot:** watch, comb
Bosun: whistle
Mrs Blackboot: hair curlers

LIGHTING PLOT

Property fittings required: nil
Exterior. A desert island

To open: Overall warm sunny lighting
No Cues

EFFECTS PLOT

Cue 1	**Children:** "You listen, Ma." *Distant music*	(Page 16)

Printed by
THE KINGFISHER PRESS, LONDON NW10 6UG

Lightning Source UK Ltd.
Milton Keynes UK
UKOW06f1025230315

248328UK00001B/8/P